ORIGINS
ORIGINS
ORIGINS
ORIGINS
ORIGINS

TWO MODELS

EVOLUTION
CREATION

RICHARD B. BLISS, M.S.

Director of Curriculum Development
Institute for Creation Research

Consulting Editors:
Duane T. Gish, Ph.D., Institute for Creation Research
John N. Moore, Ed.D., Michigan State University

CREATION·LIFE
PUBLISHERS

San Diego, California 92115

ACKNOWLEDGMENTS

I wish to express my deep gratitude to the many science teachers and students of the Unified School District in Racine, Wisconsin, for their valuable constructive review of the Origin modules, their participation in the piloting process and above all, their enthusiasm and encouragement in this truly open and scientific approach to a controversial topic.

Richard Bliss

ABOUT THE AUTHOR

Richard Bliss has been active in public school education for over 25 years. He taught chemistry, physics, biology and general science on all high school levels (7-12) and was actively engaged in curriculum development (K-12) for a number of years in the Racine, Wisconsin public school system. As Director of Science he ran continuous workshops for both high school and elementary teachers. He was adjunct professor in the University of Wisconsin system and taught science methods to prospective teachers. Bliss was the science consultant for Educational Consulting Associates, and was a free lance speaker on educational topics. Richard Bliss held several leadership positions in state and national science associations and is mentioned in Marqui's *Who's Who in Education.* Bliss received his B.S. and M.S. from the University of Wisconsin and is presently completing a doctorate from the University of Sarasota. His major fields are science and education.

TO THE STUDENT

The subject you are about to study deals with some of the most exciting problems in science. The topic of first origins has stirred the thinking of thoughtful men over the centuries and continues to do so today. Many scientists are searching for discoveries that will add information about origins, and governments are willing to spend billions of dollars to see if they can locate life on other planets. Scientists are arguing about the possibility of life ever occurring randomly, that is, by chance processes, and many are so deeply biased toward one view or another that they are unable to see the problem with an open mind.

This module will attempt to give you a good picture of the scientific "Creation" and "Evolution" viewpoints that are most popular. Your independent thoughts on this matter, after a thorough study of this material, will show your ability to think *logically,* to *search for data and its meaning,* and to *demand verification.* A searching, open mind is a free mind, and we as educators want this for students like yourself.

Richard Bliss

CONTENTS

The figure above shows how the subject of origins is viewed differently. Some have preconceived ideas (**A**) that are the result of some bias; this, of course, is a non-scientific view and results in dogma. Others look carefully at the scientific data (**B**) and try to find the model that fits it best; i.e., evolution (**C**) or creation (**D**).

INTRODUCTION

Have scientists produced evidence that tells us for certain how the earth was formed? Is there positive evidence about how life began? What about the solar system and all the things beyond; do we know how these were formed? The best answer to these questions and many others, on the basis of available scientific evidence, is that no one really knows. This kind of an answer, however, serves only to inspire the inquiring mind of man, and it is this open frontier of knowledge that often generates conflicting views, for science cannot stand alone in this matter. When we consider first origins, we cannot avoid coming face to face with **ultimate causes** and **ultimate meanings.** This involves our religious feelings.

ultimate causes: the very first responsible cause, i.e., accidental or God with all power.

ultimate meanings: why all life came to be and for what purpose.

We can't avoid the questions: Where did the creator come from? Did a creator ever exist? Answers to these questions are very simple; either he never had a beginning, or everything started from nothing and from this point everything we see came into existence. Whatever the first cause was, the student can readily see that one must apply a religious belief to an evolution or creation question. If we are going to be scientific, we must deal with only those things that we can observe or measure. When we develop our *scientific* models, they must come from the best scientific data derived from the **Processes of Science.**

Processes of Science: the skills that a scientist employs when studying a problem.

PROCESSES OF SCIENCE

1.	**Observation**	using all your senses
2.	**Classification**	placing your observations into the most logical categories
3.	**Measuring**	making careful measurements
4.	**Inference**	establishing best guesses with the information you have
5.	**Prediction**	making predictions based upon much evidence
6.	**Interpretation**	interpretation of the data you have available
7.	**Experimentation**	doing experiments to add to your knowledge
8.	**Operational Objectives**	establishing objectives that you can work with and are clearly understood
9.	**Model Building**	building temporary best models for the data you now have

model: a temporary plan. Models change with new information. Models attempt to explain how things are.

Students as well as scientists often find themselves choosing a particular **model** for origins for a variety of reasons. Some of these reasons may be as follows:

1. When the subject of origin comes up, he thinks of evolution as the only way it could happen.

2. When the subject of origins comes up, he thinks of creation as the only way it could happen.

3. He is not very familiar with evolutionary ideas.

4. He doesn't know much about the science of creation by design.

5. He honestly judges the scientific evidence after looking at both models and thinks his model fits the scientific **data** the best.

data: collection of information.

Generally speaking, these are the reasons that often come up. A scientist who is searching with an open mind would want to examine all of the *data* first and then make his decision carefully. Often we find that scientists can be carried away with their ideas; they no longer look at the data with an open mind. One model or the other is assumed to be true without further thought. It is our sincere hope that you will look at the idea of origins with a searching mind; this will keep you from having **biases** that will get in the way of real learning. The topic of origins can become very exciting when viewed this way, and there is little chance that one will become angry if he holds his *models* with a light hand. Often people become bitter and angry when their ideas can't stand testing, and they find that they cannot admit they are wrong. An **open-minded** person will guard against this and continue to look at all data when it appears.

biases: fixed ideas that prevent balanced thinking on a question.

open-minded: one whose mind is not prejudiced beforehand. One whose mind is open to new ideas.

submodels: several variations of a general model.

There are two general models of origins, "evolution" and "creation"; as you can imagine, there are **submodels** under these. Read the diagram on *page viii* along with its explanation. This should help you to understand the scientific issue better. Possibly the diagram will open your mind to a problem that can be difficult when one is engaged in an honest scientific effort.

In order to see origins in its proper relationship, a student must recognize that religion, which is outside of science, does play an important part. The following short explanation of religious views will help the student in this respect:

naturalistic: natural processes that just occur without help from any God or outside force.

mechanistic: mechanical processes. A certain way for something to happen.

According to the *atheistic evolution submodel,* there was no God involved in the process of life developing. All life arose by **naturalistic, mechanistic** processes without any direct purpose.

According to the *deistic evolution submodel,* God started the first life, and naturalistic processes allowed life to evolve into what we see today. No specific purpose is assigned to this development.

According to the *theistic evolution submodel,* God not only started the life process but directed it through all the stages of evolution; the life we see today is the result of this directed purposeful process.

According to the *creative design submodel*, all life and life processes were designed to function just as we observe them today. The designer for all of this was the God of creation. This creator not only started and designed life but also gave purpose to it.

With respect to the *submodels* and the main models, the student can see that each one depends upon some religious belief or some kind of faith. This faith may include a God or it may not. Nobody was there in the beginning, so we can only try to form intelligent ideas about what happened. A student can suppose it is just like looking at a closed black box and trying to identify its contents.

This module will not deal any further with the religious views; this is for you to ponder. It will, however, encourage you to find the model that fits the scientific data best from your own observations, or you may choose to remain neutral on the subject until more data comes in. The purpose in writing these units on origins is to enable you to make these decisions intelligently. Is the general model of evolution the best fit for the data? Is the general model of creative design the best fit for the data? No one was there, so you will have to make your own decisions after you receive the data. But first, what does the *evolutionist* say? What does the *creationist* say? What evidence does each bring forward to support his model?

A two model approach with an evolution emphasis.

CHAPTER ONE

The first chapter in this study module will deal with the "evolution" model for origins *only.* The second chapter will deal with the "creation" model *only.* These models will not be criticized except by you; they will be told as evolutionists and creationists would tell their story. When you are through, you should have a good understanding about both models. Read carefully and answer all questions to the very best of your ability.

When you have finished this chapter you will be able to:

1. **Judge whether evolution is a model that can be reasoned from scientific evidence.**

2. **Reason how the coacervate (Oparin's) hypothesis is related to the evolutionary model.**

3. **Reason how the proteinoid hypothesis (Fox) is related to the evolutionary model.**

4. **Repeat the geological evidence that supports the evolutionary model.**

5. **Show how index fossils are the key to dating geological strata by giving examples of some.**

6. **State the major time assumptions needed for evolution to occur.**

7. **Show an example of how evolution progresses over the ages (simple and complex).**

8. **State the major assumptions of the evolution model that are not supported by facts.**

9. **State the difference between a fact and an assumption.**

Figure 1.1 *Charles Robert Darwin – author of* The Origin of Species by Means of Natural Selection. *Photo taken in 1871.*

conceptual scheme: a series of ideas placed together that support a central theme.

A Model

The *model* of evolution will be referred to in this unit as an idea that explains how life developed on *planet earth.* Evolution, in its modern sense, was developed as a theory and published in a book on July 1, 1859, by Charles Darwin. At that time he presented his book on the *Origin of Species by Means of Natural Selection.* His book has had such an effect upon man's thinking that it is said: "This book has done more to alter the thinking of scientists than any other book in the last one hundred years." Figure 1.2 will give you some idea of what Darwin's model assumes.

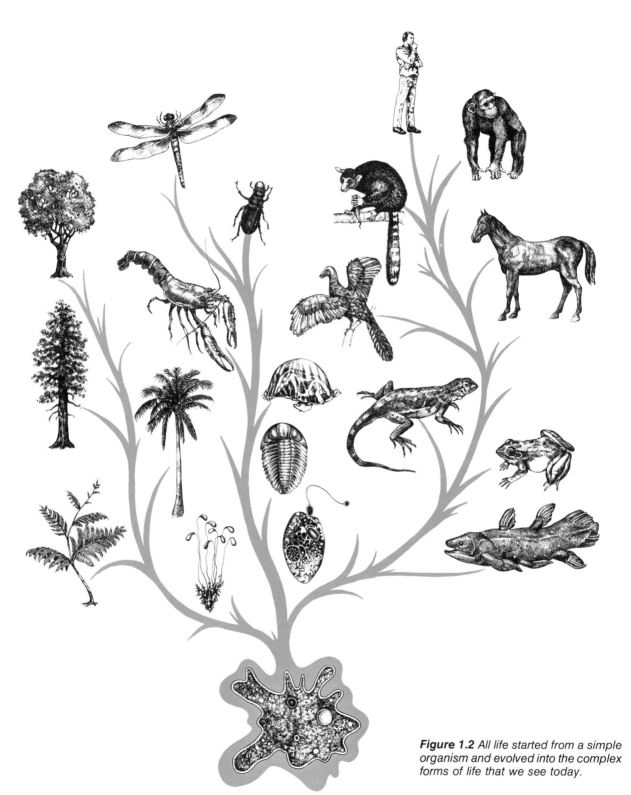

Figure 1.2 *All life started from a simple organism and evolved into the complex forms of life that we see today.*

Origins

Diversity Among Species

Diversity among **species** is caused by the various processes of evolution. A species can evolve into two or more sub-species when a portion of the population has become isolated from the group, and, no doubt, this was a very important part of the evolution of life. The evolutionist says that when a small **population** becomes separated from the parent group, changes in this population become possible. Eventually this population can no longer reproduce or breed with its ancestors and it becomes a separate species.

More specifically, different combinations of genes make the organism appear differently. Genes are various coding arrangements of the DNA molecule. When sufficiently changed, or mixed, the organism can appear quite different to the observer. Let's assume that we have a certain species population with a **gene pool** containing a mixture of genes A, B, C, and D in this pool (1); if a portion of this population (2) becomes isolated and doesn't have many of the C and D genes, it might look a little different from the original population. If this population becomes divided and the parts carry different proportions of genes, then (4) would look a little different from (5), and both (4) and (5) would look a little different from (2), and much different from (1). In some organisms (4) and (5) could eventually become new species. (See Figure 1.3).

species: a group of organisms that normally interbreed and produce fertile offspring.

population: a group of organisms which can naturally interbreed, in a given area.

gene pool: the collection of genes that exist in each reproducing population.

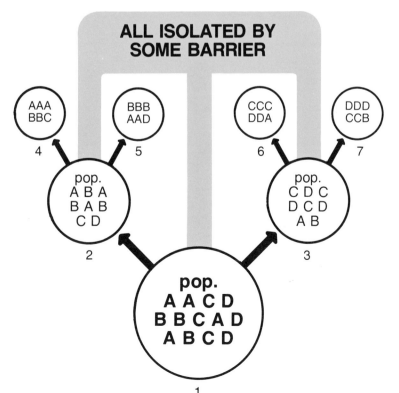

Figure 1.3 *The diagram at left shows how original gene pools can be separated. By isolating the different gene characteristics and letting* natural selection *select out the most favorable (survival of the fittest), new species could be formed.*

Scientists know that there is no way to observe big changes in evolution directly. All evidence is indirect at its best. Some very good indirect examples of evolution in action are: the peppered moth (*Biston betularia*) of Manchester, England, and the Kaibab-Abert squirrel populations in the Grand Canyon region of the Colorado River. One of these, the peppered moth, shows natural selection. The squirrels, on the other hand, show that new species have been formed by isolation.

The case of the peppered moth (see *Scientific American,* Jan., 1975), has been called the most striking example of evolution ever seen by man. Before 1845 the moth was mostly light-colored, with dark blotches and spots. Most of the trees on which the moth rested had light gray bark. You can imagine that a moth colored like this would be difficult to see against its background. A few of these peppered moths, however, were dark in color (known as the melanic or carbonaria form). They were easy to see against a light background. Naturally, birds ate more of the dark-colored variety than the light-colored variety, simply because they could see them more easily. Thus, the peppered moth population was predominantly made up of the light-colored variety (see Figure 1.4).

Figure 1.4a (below left) The light-colored variety and the dark-colored variety of Biston betularia at rest on a soot-covered oak trunk near Birmingham, England. *Figure 1.4b* and <u>Biston betularia</u> at rest on a lichen-covered tree trunk in the unpolluted English countryside.

But with the onset of the industrial revolution, soot and other **contaminants** polluted the air and the tree trunks became progressively darker. Eventually, it was the light-colored variety of moths that became easy to see while resting on the darkened tree trunks and the dark-colored variety became difficult to see; thus birds began to eat more of the light-colored and fewer of the dark-colored variety. As a consequence, today most of these peppered moths consist of the dark-colored variety.[1] Some scientists consider this a classical example of **natural selection** which produced evolution from a light to dark *Biston betularia* moth.

contaminant: material that makes the environment less pure. (Soot, dust, sulfur dioxide, etc., in this case.)

natural selection: the elimination of the unfit and the survival of the fit in the struggle for existence.

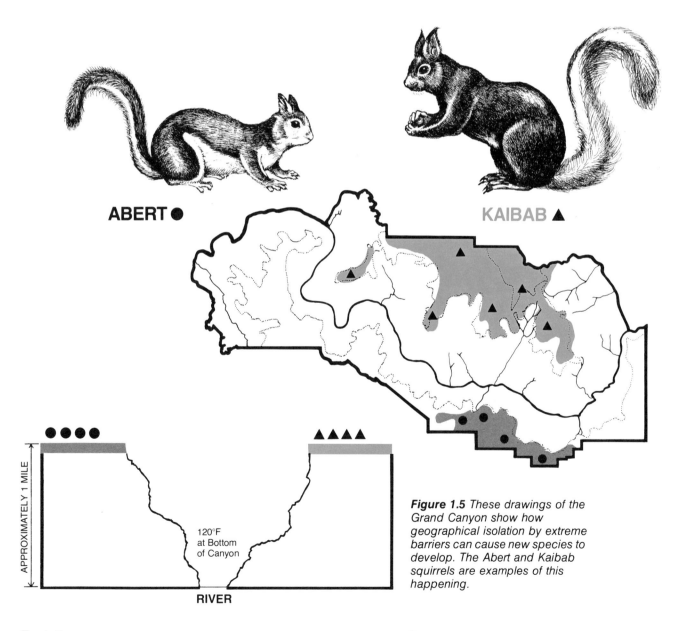

ABERT ●

KAIBAB ▲

Figure 1.5 *These drawings of the Grand Canyon show how geographical isolation by extreme barriers can cause new species to develop. The Abert and Kaibab squirrels are examples of this happening.*

120°F at Bottom of Canyon

APPROXIMATELY 1 MILE

RIVER

Evolution

9

Let us now consider the case of the Kaibab squirrel. Here we see two squirrel populations that became separated by a large canyon; a fast flowing river winds through the bottom of the canyon, and temperatures here reach 120°F in the summer. These barriers separated the two populations so they could not rejoin. The *gene pools* were separated; mutations in each group caused further variations and thousands of years passed. Soon the populations became much different, as we see them today through processes of adaption and *natural selection*. This has been described as an excellent example of evolution occurring.

Before you go further, try to state a hypothesis of your own about how these organisms became different.

Species

How do new species form? The mechanisms of **variation, mutation, migration, isolation,** and **natural selection** help an organism to adapt, and all contribute to the formation of new species. Imagine the first maple tree as one kind of tree. How, then, did modern maple trees become so different? Evolutionists believe that mutations and adaptations in the original group allowed some to survive in wet areas and others to survive in dry areas. The silver maple is a good example of this kind of change in the evolution of plants.

variation: a difference in the structure or character of an organism from that of others of the same species or group.

mutation: a change or alteration in a gene.

migration: animals moving from one place to another.

isolation: separation of populations from the main population.

Figure 1.6 *In all of these animals, similarities of structure can be traced to the little shrew-like mammal in the center. This is called adaptive radiation.*

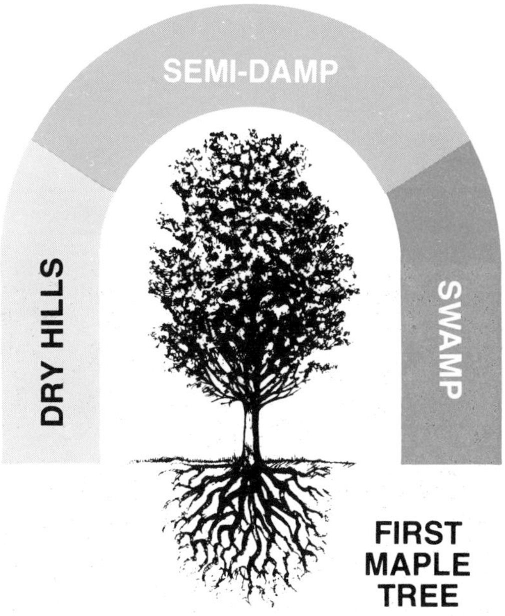

SEMI-DAMP

DRY HILLS

SWAMP

FIRST MAPLE TREE

Figure 1.7 *The maple tree shows adaption to different environments.*

"**Adaptive radiation**" is the more correct term for the example used above. This is very important in the evolution *model.* Evolutionists believe that many varieties of plants and animals were formed this way.

Many examples could be given that would show observations such as those above, but how did it all start? What strange set of events could produce different kinds of living things in this manner?

adaptive radiation: evolution from a single ancestral species, of a variety of forms which occupy different habitats.

Evolution

Prebiological Evolution

According to the evolution model there was a time when no life of any kind existed on the earth. Some scientists believe that the atmosphere at that time contained a mixture of simple gases; they believe that this atmosphere could not have been the same as the atmosphere is today. Now we have much free oxygen in the atmosphere (the present atmosphere contains 78% nitrogen, 21% oxygen, and 1% of other gases, including carbon dioxide, water vapor, argon, and small amounts of other gases). If the primitive atmosphere contained **free oxygen**, everything would have been **oxidized**, and none of the chemical compounds necessary for the origin of life could have existed (see Figure 1.8). All of the carbon, for example, would have been oxidized to carbon dioxide. Evolutionists thus believe that the original atmosphere was reducing (no free oxygen) instead of oxidizing (containing free oxygen) as our present atmosphere is.

free oxygen: oxygen that is not bound to any other element.

oxidized: combined with oxygen.

Figure 1.8 This illustration shows a reducing atmosphere as it may have appeared, and the oxidizing atmosphere as it appears today.

METHANE   (CH₄)
AMMONIA   (NH₃)
HYDROGEN   (H₂)
WATER VAPOR   (H₂O)

REDUCING

WATER VAPOR   (H₂O)
OXYGEN   (O₂)
CARBON DIOXIDE   (CO₂)
NITROGEN   (N₂)

OXIDIZING

There would have been plenty of energy available on the primitive earth, most of it coming from the **ultraviolet light** of the sun, and some from lightning, heat, radioactivity, etc. According to evolution theory, this energy acted on the simple gases in the atmosphere to produce organic chemical compounds, such as amino acids and sugars. After enough of such compounds had been produced, they could have combined to form large, complicated molecules like proteins and DNA; these, of course, are the kinds of molecules necessary for life to form. Finally, according to evolution theory, these molecules somehow got together in a cooperative system, enclosed themselves with a membrane, and life began.

In 1953 Stanley Miller along with Harold C. Urey performed an experiment which seems to support the above **hypothesis.** They put a mixture of methane, ammonia, hydrogen, and water vapor in an apparatus which had a sparking chamber (see Figure 1.9a) to supply energy. The sparking chamber imitated lightning. After the mixture of gases had been sparked for a week or two, a few amino acids were detected in the solution which had collected in a cold trap. Amino acids are the sub-units or building blocks that link up in long chains to form proteins. Evolutionists say that the Miller-Urey experiment gives us some idea of how **amino acids** and other simple organic chemical compounds may have formed on the primitive earth.

ultraviolet light: short wave, high energy light.

hypothesis: an idea set forth as an explanation for a set of observations.

amino acids: the chemical building blocks of proteins.

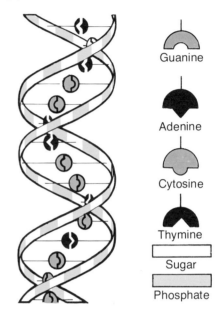

Figure 1.10 *(above) The diagram shows the DNA molecule as it might be coded for a specific protein.*

Figure 1.9a *The Urey and Miller apparatus looked something like this diagram. The mixture of special chemicals was heated – sparked with high voltage – cooled back into a liquid and the product (amino acids, etc.) was drawn off at the cold trap.*

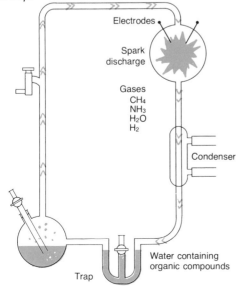

Figure 1.9b *(right) Stanley Miller with his famous apparatus.*

Even earlier than the Miller-Urey experiment, a Russian biochemist, A. I. Oparin, suggested that the preliminary stages in the formation of the first living cell may have been *gel-like* masses called **coacervates.** He believes these tiny balls of jell-like material may have absorbed (soaked up) chemicals from the surroundings. If enzymes, DNA, and other biological molecules were nearby, they would have been absorbed into the coacervates and led to more and more complex organizations until finally the first cell came into existence.

coacervates: combinations of two complex compounds, such as proteins and fats, which separate out of solution to form tiny gel-like ball

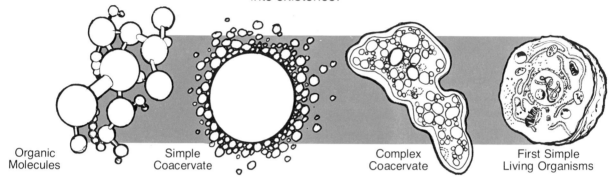

Organic Molecules   Simple Coacervate   Complex Coacervate   First Simple Living Organisms

Figure 1.11 *A. I. Oparin's coacervates seemed to grow from simple to complex.*

Another idea came from an American biochemist, Sidney Fox. He heated a pure dry mixture of amino acids at 175°C (water boils at 100°C) for a few hours. When the product was dissolved in hot water and the mixture was allowed to cool, tiny droplets formed which Fox calls proteinoid microspheres. These microspheres contain **polymers** of amino acids which he believes have at least slight biological activity (enzyme activity). He also believes that they could

polymers: chemical compounds or mixtures consisting of repeating structural units. Example: amino acids hooked together in long chains to make large molecules.

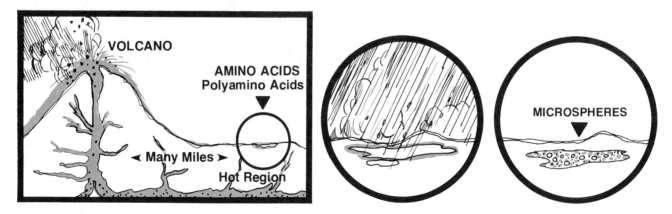

Figure 1.12 *Fox's theory requires that amino acids be subjected to a great deal of heat (175°C). These amino acids would form polymers; be washed away (between 4-8 hours) by rain; collect in an isolated pool; and form proteinoids which would evolve into living cells. Fox claims that these proteinoid substances had living characteristics.*

have absorbed more material and become progressively more complex until the first cell came into existence.

All of these ideas have been placed together to form a hypothesis which evolutionists believe is the most reasonable guess about how chemical evolution occurred and led up to the first living cell.

Figure 1.13 This diagram shows the evolutionary model as it predicts life having evolved from the simple to the complex forms that we know today.

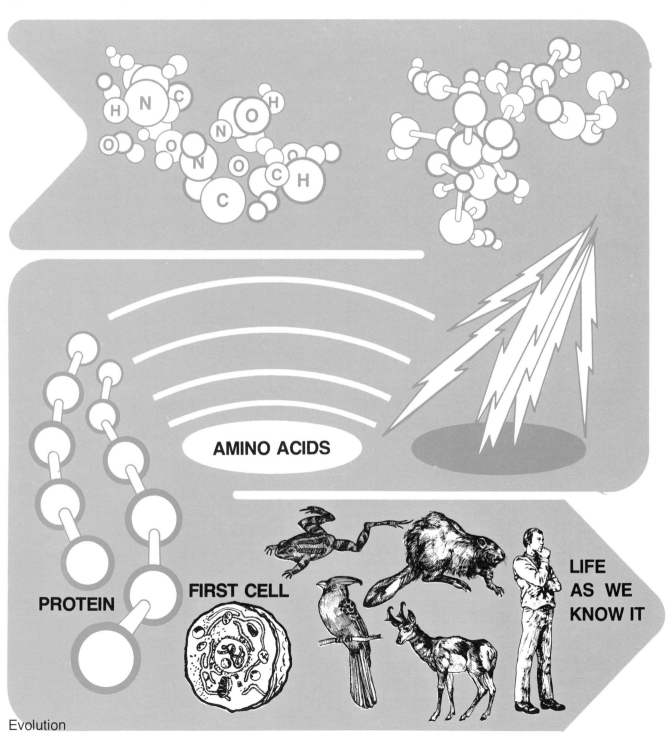

AMINO ACIDS

PROTEIN

FIRST CELL

LIFE AS WE KNOW IT

1. Comment on the earth's first atmosphere, from your own thinking.

2. Which idea about first *pre-life* seems the most reasonable to you? (Oparin — Fox — Miller)

3. Why do some pre-life researchers start with amino acids?

4. What chance do you think there is of the first cell occurring by random (accidental) processes?

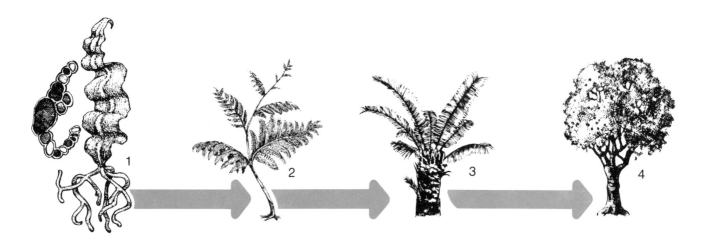

Figure 1.14 *Algae (plants with chlorophyll) (1) evolved into more complex green plants like mosses and ferns (2); these evolved into cycads and other gymnosperms (3) and finally into the kinds of complex flowering plants we see today (4).*

Biological Evolution

Evolutionists feel that the first living cell was much simpler than an ameba. Perhaps the first cell was like bacteria which depend upon the environment for their food, only much simpler. As these tiny cells struggled for existence, a new kind of cell, able to produce its own food, like algae, began to evolve. **Heterotrophs,** like bacteria, which feed on others, could now feed on **autotrophs,** like the algae, which make their own food. This took place early in the evolution of living things.

Through the process of natural selection and adaptation these organisms continued to evolve. More complex organisms began to appear and the process of continuing evolution went on. Figures 1.14, 1.15, 1.16, and 1.17 give an idea of how evolution in plants and animals occurred.

heterotrophs: organisms that depend on other organisms for their food.

autotrophs: organisms that can produce their own food using sunlight for energy.

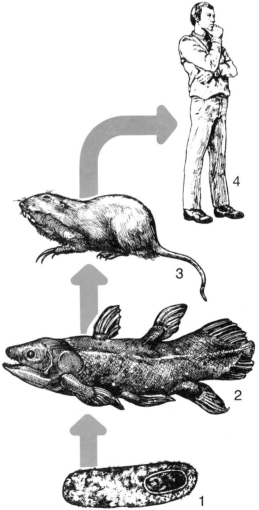

Figure 1.16 Heterotrophs *(bacteria) (1), evolved into more complex multicellular organisms which eventually evolved into fish (2); the fish evolved into amphibia which evolved into reptiles and finally into mammals (3); the mammals evolved into what we see today, including man (4).*

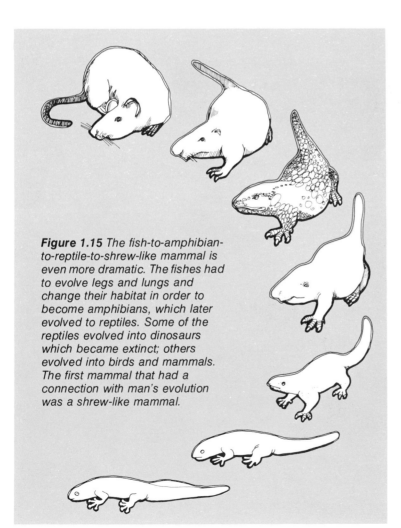

Figure 1.15 *The fish-to-amphibian-to-reptile-to-shrew-like mammal is even more dramatic. The fishes had to evolve legs and lungs and change their habitat in order to become amphibians, which later evolved to reptiles. Some of the reptiles evolved into dinosaurs which became extinct; others evolved into birds and mammals. The first mammal that had a connection with man's evolution was a shrew-like mammal.*

Evolution

Many organisms were successful for a while, but eventually failed in their evolutionary climb; others, however, continued to succeed. Evolutionists assume that many billions of unlikely events occurred during the evolution of all life toward what we see today.

Mammals are believed to have evolved from reptiles. Evolution made it possible for reptiles to reconstruct their jaws, change their skin and method of reproduction and finally become mammals. Birds had a more difficult job as they evolved from the land and adapted to flight. The reptile ancestors of birds evolved feathers from their scales. Wings were also an evolutionary problem; but in spite of all the odds, they made it. More recent theories indicate that warm-blooded dinosaurs (usually thought to be cold-blooded) were the ancestors of birds.[2]

Figure 1.17a *Illustration showing lizards in natural surroundings.*

[2]A complete story of this evidence can be found in *Scientific American*, April, 1975, p. 58.

1. What kinds of things would have to happen for algae to evolve into a tree? (your ideas on the subject)

2. What kinds of problems would a reptile have as he evolved to become archaeopteryx?

3. List the facts and the guesswork that must be a part of the evolution of archaeopteryx.

4. What is the key factor that makes evolution possible?

Figure 1.17b *Illustration showing a hypothetical lizard evolving toward Archaeopteryx.*

Index Fossils

Evolutionists point to the geologic column for evidence to support their model. They claim that the simplest forms of life can be found in the oldest strata. As time went on, more complex forms evolved, and these are found in the younger geologic strata. Whether a certain stratum is old or young is determined primarily by the kind of fossils that it contains. These all important fossils are called **index fossils.** An index fossil that is supposed to be relatively simple in structure, such as a sponge, would be considered very old, and thus the strata in which it is found would be considered very old also. Figure 1.18 will give you some idea of how this system works.

index fossils: certain fossils that identify strata or earth layers

**GEOLOGICAL COLUMN
Index Fossils**

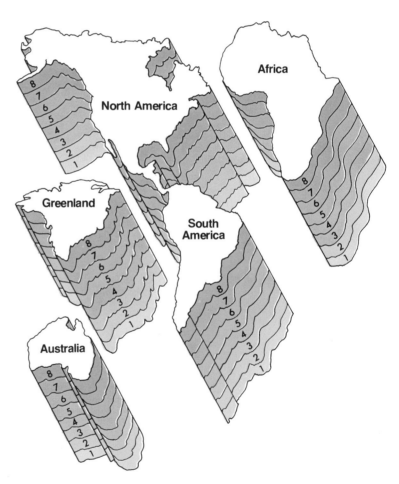

Figure 1.18a This illustration shows the geologic column and how index fossils can identify these layers.

Origins

MAJOR DIVISIONS OF GEOLOGIC TIME   INDEX FOSSILS

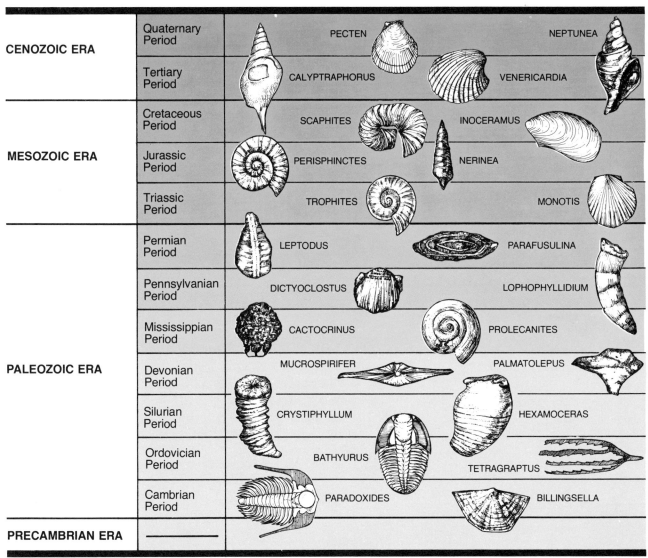

CENOZOIC ERA	Quaternary Period	PECTEN NEPTUNEA
	Tertiary Period	CALYPTRAPHORUS VENERICARDIA
MESOZOIC ERA	Cretaceous Period	SCAPHITES INOCERAMUS
	Jurassic Period	PERISPHINCTES NERINEA
	Triassic Period	TROPHITES MONOTIS
PALEOZOIC ERA	Permian Period	LEPTODUS PARAFUSULINA
	Pennsylvanian Period	DICTYOCLOSTUS LOPHOPHYLLIDIUM
	Mississippian Period	CACTOCRINUS PROLECANITES
	Devonian Period	MUCROSPIRIFER PALMATOLEPUS
	Silurian Period	CRYSTIPHYLLUM HEXAMOCERAS
	Ordovician Period	BATHYURUS TETRAGRAPTUS
	Cambrian Period	PARADOXIDES BILLINGSELLA
PRECAMBRIAN ERA		

Figure 1.18b

Time Clocks

Evolution depends upon billions of years of time because the various processes take a long time. There are certain kinds of time clocks that are believed to tell the age of the earth and give scientists better clues for great amounts of time. The uranium-lead clocks are among the best known. They are supposed to work just like an hour glass. The scientist knows that uranium changes or "decays" into lead, so he measures the amount of uranium and lead in his sample and from this he is able to calculate its age. Scientists have dated many very old rocks with this technique.

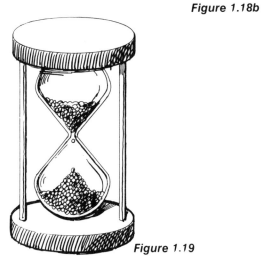

Figure 1.19

Evolution

21

The uranium clocks that seem to indicate that the earth is around 4.5 billion years old. This should not be confused with the dating of strata by fossils, however, for uranium clocks are seldom used to date **fossil strata.** Uranium-lead dating is not the only method used by scientists; other methods such as potassium-argon are used to date material, but all are keyed in on or adjusted to the uranium-lead clock.

fossil strata: sedimentary strata that contain fossils of plants and animals.

1. How can scientists know the age of the different geologic strata?
2. How can scientists know the age of index fossils?
3. How can scientists know the age of the earth?

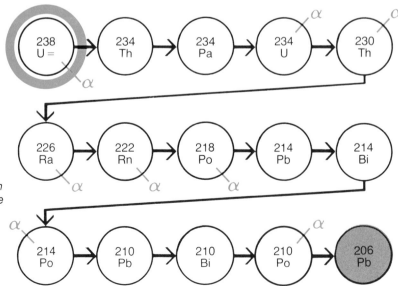

Figure 1.20 The drawing at right shows how uranium (U-238) decays to lead (Pb-206). Certain time calculations can be made by observing the amount of U-238 and Pb-206 in the sample.

Origins

Man and Evolution

How did man come on the scene? From what did he evolve? What evidence do we have to show man's evolution? The story is very uncertain because of the few fossils that we have of man.

The evolutionary story of man starts with **Australopithecus,** several million years ago. There is uncertainty here, but if we arranged man-like skulls in order, they would appear something like this:

Australopithecus: "Southern Ape" thought to have ape and man-like features.

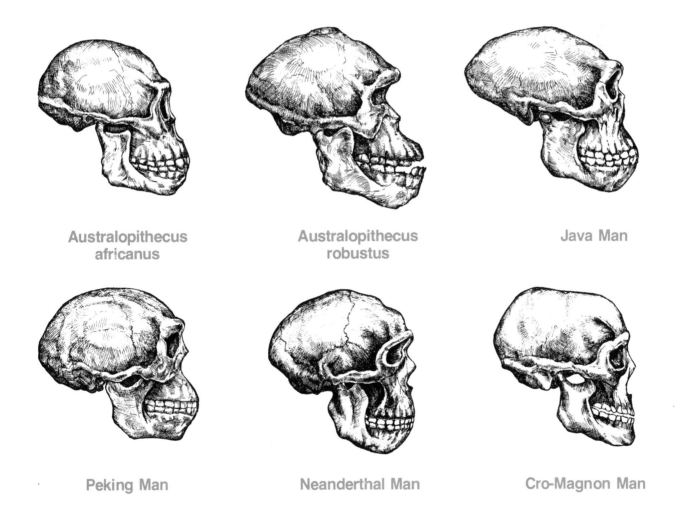

Australopithecus africanus

Australopithecus robustus

Java Man

Peking Man

Neanderthal Man

Cro-Magnon Man

Figure 1.21 This is the order in which some scientists believe man evolved.

Many scientists feel that the evolution of man occurred just as with any other organism; they believe that man has developed his heritage from his animal ancestry and that his evolving brain allowed him to progress faster than other creatures. The branches of the evolutionary story that resulted in man is thought to be something like the following:

Figure 1.22 Evolutionary tree from pre-man to modern man.

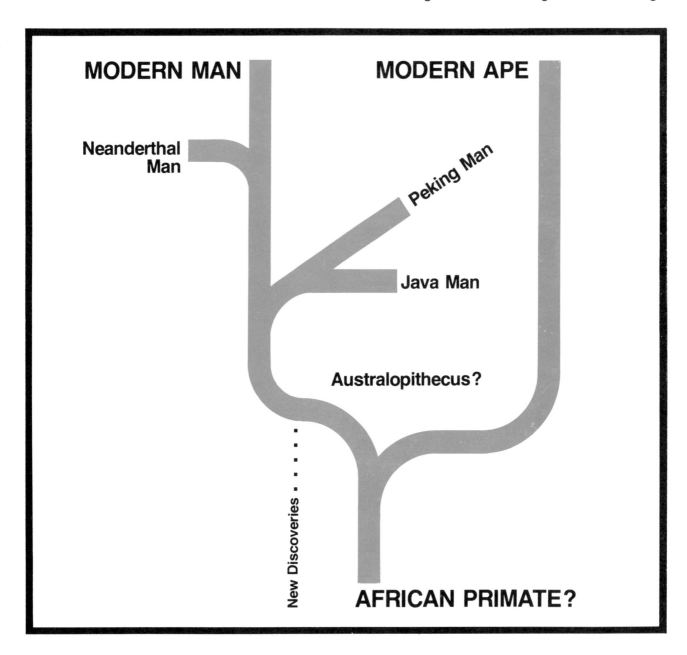

Interested students will want to watch new discoveries closely; many things are appearing that could alter the branches of this tree.

1. Do you think new discoveries of man's ancestors will continue to support the branches in Figure 1.22?
2. What are your opinions about man's evolution?

Homology

This is a good time to discuss **homology,** a technique that is used to show relationships of animal parts. Some scientists are firmly convinced of these relationships and use them to strengthen the evolution model.

In the case of the reptile "hinge bones" (Figure 1.24), a person might wonder about its disappearance in mammals. The evolutionist points out that these bones have become two tiny "ear bones" in the mammal (incus and malleus). Yes, it is believed that during millions of years of the evolutionary process this sensational change has occurred.

Figure 1.23 These limb bones from different mammals are said to homologous, or similar in structure and therefore related.

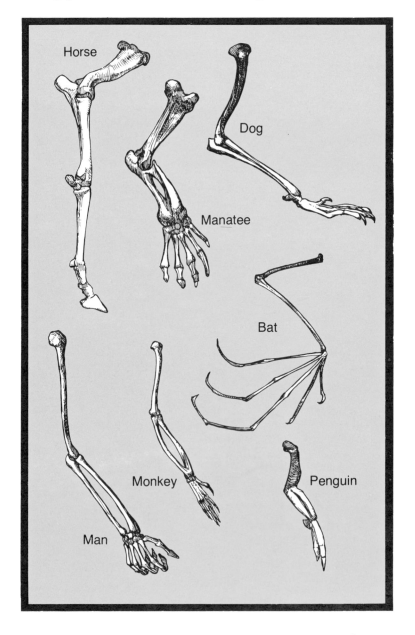

Origins

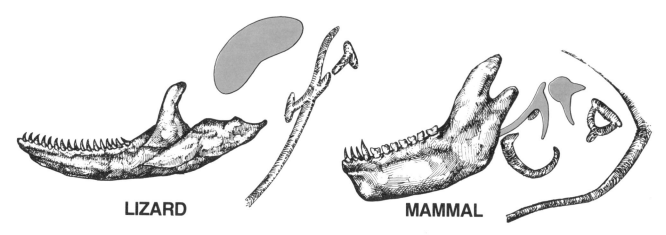

LIZARD **MAMMAL**

Figure 1.24 Evolution of the reptile "hinge bone" into the mammalian ear bones (homologous structures).

Many feel that the relationships of the bones shown in Figure 1.23 have evolved through the ages by evolution from a common ancestor. Notice the finger-like shape of the bat-wing and man's arm, the manatee front leg and the dog and monkey front leg. Evolution offers an explanation for this agreement (homology) between organs. Evolutionists are convinced that plant homologies, such as those in Figure 1.25, give strong evidence to past history.

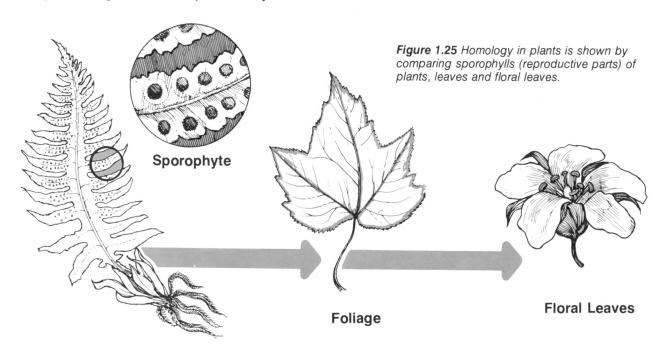

Sporophyte

Foliage

Floral Leaves

Figure 1.25 Homology in plants is shown by comparing sporophylls (reproductive parts) of plants, leaves and floral leaves.

In some plants that are primitive, these parts seem to be homologous; therefore, evolutionists reason that they have a common ancestor.

Evolution

1. How long do you think it would take for natural selection, mutations, and adaptations to evolve jaw bones to ear bones?

2. Which of all the homologies seem most reasonable to you? (Figure 1.23, 1.24, 1.25, or some other combination)

3. Give your own ideas about homologies and evolution.

Summary

This is only a general view of how evolution could have occurred; there are many other parts included in the evolution model that evolutionists think are support for their claims, such as biochemical likeness of species, etc. These will be discussed more thoroughly in a separate module.

You have heard only one side of the story related to life's origin. Wise persons will withhold judgment until they have heard all the evidence for both models of origins. Continue on with your study in Chapter Two and see if you can find the important differences in the two models.

A two model approach with a creation emphasis.

CHAPTER TWO

This unit will deal with some of the more popular parts of the creation model of origins *only*. When you have finished you will be able to:

1. Judge whether creation is a *model* that can be reasoned from scientific evidence.

2. Understand how creative design is related to the creation model.

3. State the evidence indicating that the most primitive atmosphere was an oxidizing atmosphere similar to today's atmosphere.

4. Reason why creationists believe that it is chemically impossible for the simple cell to occur by chance.

5. Reason that the simple cell is a perfectly designed chemical system.

6. List the geologic evidence that supports the creation model.

7. Understand the earth age studies that support a creation model.

8. Reason why the creation model depends upon supernatural events.

9. State the major assumptions of the creation model that are not supported by facts.

model: a temporary plan. Models change with new information. Models attempt to explain how things are.

The construction of the creation model will be based upon scientific evidence that supports creation and flood geology. The creation model, in its modern sense, has been developed scientifically by scientists who interpret present scientific data about life as the result of *original design*.

According to the creation model, all living things originated from basic **kinds** of life, each of which was separately created. From these basic kinds of life, all of the known diversity in living things originated. All of the genetic possibilities for differences in man, dog, cat, frog, tree, flower, etc., were found within the **gene pool** of these organisms.

kind: an original created type of plant or animal that did not arise from any other type.

Look around you: are there differences between the students in your class? Are there differences between brothers and sisters within a family? How many groups could you place man into, based upon color, shape, size, etc? Is this true of all other life? The photograph in Figure 2.2 will give a better idea of how this looks.

gene pool: the collection of genes that exist in each reproducing kind of organism.

Figure 2.1 *The different kinds of animals and plants can vary considerably within the genetic limits of each kind. However, one kind of animal becoming another kind is never seen.*

Origins

Figure 2.2 *A person can see much variation within the human race. The creationist predicts that this is the result of a complex original gene pool.*

1. Describe, from your knowledge, how a kind of organism (frogs, dogs, cats, etc.) could or could not produce all the varieties we see today.

2. Would all humans be placed in the same basic kind by creationists?

3. List at least four ways that a brother, sister, or mother looks different than you.

4. List ten ways that your best friend looks different than you.

The Record

One idea about how the universe and life first came upon the scene is that all things were originated by a creator. The Biblical account of creation as accepted by many Jews, Moslems, and Christians is one of several such accounts which agree with this theory. Many scientists claim that the variety of life we now see could have come from the first original created kinds of organisms. The following pages will show how creationists believe scientific data seem to support this idea.

The creationist maintains that the record shows that life exploded into existence all of a sudden. He also observes that this record doesn't follow a pattern of simple to complex life. A look at the **strata** reveals that even in the **Cambrian**

strata: layers of rock built on top of each other.

Cambrian: considered to be the oldest formation where complex traces of life can be found.

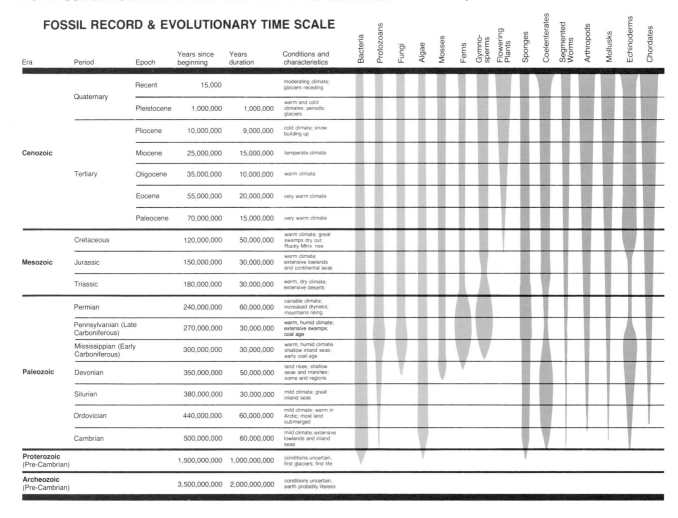

FOSSIL RECORD & EVOLUTIONARY TIME SCALE

Era	Period	Epoch	Years since beginning	Years duration	Conditions and characteristics
Cenozoic	Quaternary	Recent	15,000		moderating climate; glaciers receding
		Pleistocene	1,000,000	1,000,000	warm and cold climates; periodic glaciers
	Tertiary	Pliocene	10,000,000	9,000,000	cold climate; snow building up
		Miocene	25,000,000	15,000,000	temperate climate
		Oligocene	35,000,000	10,000,000	warm climate
		Eocene	55,000,000	20,000,000	very warm climate
		Paleocene	70,000,000	15,000,000	very warm climate
Mesozoic	Cretaceous		120,000,000	50,000,000	warm climate; great swamps dry out; Rocky Mtns. rise
	Jurassic		150,000,000	30,000,000	warm climate; extensive lowlands and continental seas
	Triassic		180,000,000	30,000,000	warm, dry climate; extensive deserts
Paleozoic	Permian		240,000,000	60,000,000	variable climate; increased dryness; mountains rising
	Pennsylvanian (Late Carboniferous)		270,000,000	30,000,000	warm, humid climate; extensive swamps; coal age
	Mississippian (Early Carboniferous)		300,000,000	30,000,000	warm, humid climate; shallow inland seas; early coal age
	Devonian		350,000,000	50,000,000	land rises; shallow seas and marshes; some arid regions
	Silurian		380,000,000	30,000,000	mild climate; great inland seas
	Ordovician		440,000,000	60,000,000	mild climate; warm in Arctic; most land submerged
	Cambrian		500,000,000	60,000,000	mild climate; extensive lowlands and inland seas
Proterozoic (Pre-Cambrian)			1,500,000,000	1,000,000,000	conditions uncertain, first glaciers, first life
Archeozoic (Pre-Cambrian)			3,500,000,000	2,000,000,000	conditions uncertain, earth probably lifeless

Column headers: Bacteria, Protozoans, Fungi, Algae, Mosses, Ferns, Gymnosperms, Flowering Plants, Sponges, Coelenterates, Segmented Worms, Arthropods, Mollusks, Echinoderms, Chordates

Figure 2.3 *Table shows fossil record and time scale as it can be found in the geologic column. The time sequences shown are evolutionary assumptions.*

layers, which are assumed to be very old by evolutionists (see Figure 2.3), many forms of complex life were present, and ancestors cannot be found in older rocks. In addition, there is no evidence, creationists believe, that one of a kind life changed into something else over a vast period of time. Study the chart of plant and animal life in the geologic column shown in Figure 2.3.

Creationists consider most of the vast **sedimentary** layers of rock covering the earth today to have been deposited by a flood. These flood waters came quickly and destroyed almost all of the animal life and much of the land plant life. This flood covered the highest mountains. The evidence for a *global* flood includes continent-wide sedimentary formations along with vast fossil graveyards. This, of course, is in conflict with a gradual formation of the geologic formations. Many studies made by geologists give good reason for doubting the standard interpretation of the **geologic record.** These studies indicate that the earth's sediments do not seem to have been deposited over long periods of time, but rather short periods of time. In any account, the time periods are too short for anything other than creation to have occurred.

sedimentary: formed from loose particles or chemicals deposited on the earth's surface, usually by the action of water.

geologic record: the interpretation of the factors found in rocks to produce a timetable.

1. **Look carefully at the geologic record. What do you think this record tells about first origins?**

2. **From the information in Figure 2.3, what places show one organism becoming something else? (an amphibian becoming a reptile or something like that)**

3. **What kind of evidence in the geologic column would be most helpful to an evolutionist student of origins? A creationist student? (from your own knowledge)**

Origins

A Flood

Flood geologists have formed some ideas of how these deposits were made. They state that if a person looks at the record, he will notice that a flood interpretation seems to fit the scientific data best.

Figure 2.4 Stages of the catastrophic flood as understood by creationists.

STAGE 1

Violent earth movements (faulting) on the ocean floor, bursting open underground water reservoirs, generated ocean waves which inundated the land surface.

STAGE 2

Torrential rain and the gushing of subterranean water continued until the flood waters engulfed continents. Millions of organisms were buried by sand, lime, and mud.

STAGE 3

Sedimentary strata with fossils were also formed during the retreat of the flood water.

STAGE 4

As the oceans assumed their present basins, canyons were eroded in the soft sediments, mountains were uplifted, and a cooler climate began to prevail. The ice age was an after-effect of the flood.

As the flood waters were rushing forth and produced a complicated mix of materials, the higher **density** objects and the objects that were more streamlined, such as sea shells, etc., settled out first. The land animals that could move quickly went to the higher ground. Many of these animals at higher levels were eventually trapped and buried. Fishes, worms, etc., were quickly buried in the sediment (see Figure 2.4). The creationist points out that the type of fossils found in a particular area is in keeping with the **ecological habitat** in which this life would be found. For example, *Cambrian* rocks were actually formed by the burial of bottom-dwelling sea animals. Creationists believe that

density: the weight of a substance in relation to its volume.

ecological habitat: community or ecosystem that an organism inhabits.

Devonian: one of the earlier periods shown in geologic life.

sediments: material that has been deposited, usually from water.

these would be buried first during a flood followed by successive strata.

Some of the greatest deposits are the **Devonian** fish beds; fossil graveyards in Agate Springs, Nebraska; and many others. The Nebraska graveyards look something like the picture in Figure 2.6. Creation scientists say that a flood is the most likely explanation for these finds. The creationists point out additional facts such as those listed below to support their model. (See Figure 2.7-2.8 also).

1. Almost all *sediments* **that contain fossils were probably water deposited.**

2. Great underwater canyons around every continent in the world indicate a rushing and gouging of water.

3. 750,000 square miles of sediment thousands of feet thick was found on the Tibetan Plateau three miles high. Creationists feel that the best explanation for this would be a great flood.

4. Continent wide sedimentary layers of sandstone, limestone, and shale could only have been deposited by water on a large scale.

Figure 2.5 *Map shows the wide distribution of one sandstone stratum (St. Peter sandstone) in the United States. This is typical of many water deposits of sediments throughout the world that seem to support a world-wide flood concept.*

38   Origins

5. Fossil deposits all over the world can be found out of their assumed evolutionary geologic order. Deposits in Virginia, Pennsylvania, Illinois, Missouri, Kentucky, and other places are examples of this.

6. The existence of vast fossil graveyards are known. It has been estimated that the Karoo Formation of South Africa contains the fossils of 800 billion vertebrates, such as reptiles.

Figure 2.6a (above left) This rock slab was taken from the well-known "bone bed" at Agate Springs, Nebraska, a stratum in which fossil bones of thousands of mammals have been found. The bone layer runs horizontally for a large distance in the limestone hill, and has evidently been water-laid. Fossils of the rhinoceros, camel, giant bear, and numerous other exotic animals are found jumbled together in this stratum. Figure 2.6b (above right) Looking west down onto bones, Agate Springs quarry.

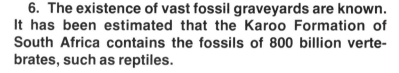

TILL

CHALK

SLIDE ROCK

Figure 2.7 "120 million year old" Cretaceous (chalk) and "1 million year old" Pleistocene mixed together in England.

Figure 2.8 *World's most widespread coal seam (Croweburg, Colchester, and Lower Kittanning coals from the middle Pennsylvanian System).*

Area Covered by Coal Equals Approx.
160,000 Square Miles

7. **Coal formations were no doubt formed from vast amounts of plant material transported by water and sediment. Finally, the material was buried. See the coal field map in Figure 2.8.**

Recent experiments have shown that coal and oil can be formed in a very short time (minutes to hours) under heat and pressure. Perhaps this tells us something about the age of our coal fields.

1. **Give two ideas that you think could be reasonable explanations for vast graveyards of bones throughout the world.**
2. **What interpretation could you give for fossils being out of their assumed geological order?**

Kinds and Variations

All life came from basic *kinds.* Each kind had stored up within it a vast *gene pool.* With this vast pool for heredity change it was possible for the plant and animal varieties that we see today to develop within each kind. A good example of what this means can be shown in Figure 2.9.

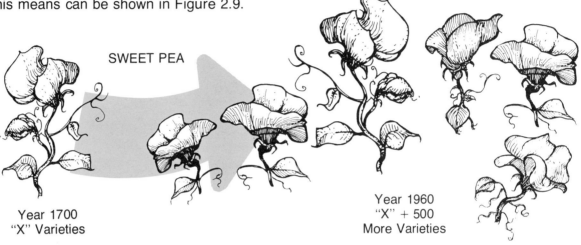

SWEET PEA

Year 1700
"X" Varieties

Year 1960
"X" + 500
More Varieties

Year 1700
"X" Dog Varieties

Year 1960
"X" + 200 More Varieties

Utilizing the gene pool, or genetic variability within each one of the kinds, such as the sweet pea and the wild or mongrel dog, man has sorted out these genetic differences so that in a very short time he has produced many varieties of sweet peas, dogs, pigeons, horses, cows, etc. Imagine what could happen in many thousands of years, even without man's help. Scientists claim that if two individuals differ by only seven pairs of genes, the number of **variations** will be 16,384 scattered between 2,187 genetic types. It would seem that in a relatively short period of time the many

Figure 2.9 Since 1700 A.D. an increase in pea varieties of over 500 have been observed. From the very first mongrel dog we now have 200 additional varieties of dog.

variations: differences in the structure or character of an organism from that of others of the same species or group.

shapes and sizes of plants and animals within each kind could have arisen. But in every case we always see that a dog remains a dog, a tree remains a tree, a man remains a man. No one has ever seen one form of life become something different, such as a reptile becoming a bird (see Figures 2:10a and 2:10b).

Figure 2.10a The concept of many varieties of plant and animal life from a specific kind is well supported by factual observation. (Galapagos Island Finches)

mutation: a change or alteration in a gene.

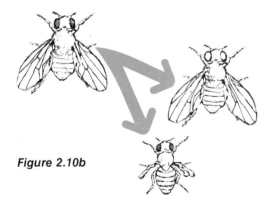

Figure 2.10b

transitional forms: plants and animals with structures and parts that seem to be turning into something else.

Other examples may be pointed out. The fruit fly, *Drosophila,* has been studied through more than 1500 generations. It has been treated with x-rays and other means to speed up the **mutation** rate. These mutations cause many kinds of changes to take place. White-eyed flies, flies with partial eyes, blind flies, sterile flies, flies with stubby wings, flies with no wings, etc. have been produced. A lot of bad flies have been produced, but never a better fly. And the fruit fly always remains a fruit fly (see Figure 2.10b).

Thus, while man has been able to select certain combinations of genes to derive many varieties of dogs, pigeons, cows, wheat, and corn, he cannot change a dog into a cat or a pigeon into a canary. Each kind remains the same basic kind no matter how much shuffling and reshuffling of the genes is carried out.

Creationists also point out that among the two million or more species of plants and animals now living on the earth, there are no **transitional forms** to be found which would indicate something other than creation happened. No examples of any such partly formed organs can be found among these millions of species. All organs and structures are fully formed and fully functional.

Creationists believe that one of the most convincing scientific facts that supports the creation model and contradicts any other model is the abrupt appearance in the

Origins

fossil record of each one of the basic kinds, as well as the lack of ancient ancestors and transitional forms between these basic kinds.

Earlier in this chapter it was pointed out that there are fossils of many different kinds of complex animals, such as *sponges, trilobites, jellyfishes, worms, sea urchins, brachiopods,* and various kinds of *mollusks* and *crustaceans,* which are found in Cambrian rocks or strata. These animals are complex and seem to be designed so well that it is difficult to imagine anything other than a created organism in each case. We will go into more detail on this very interesting topic in the module on geology. Creationists maintain further that there are no transitional forms between basically different kinds of plants and animals in the record.

Examples of big gaps in the fossil record between fishes and amphibians (there are no transitional forms with part-way fins and part-way feet) and between non-flying animals and the flying animals are observed. Four kinds of flying animals are known — birds, flying insects, flying reptiles (now extinct), and flying mammals (bats). In each case, the fossils of these flying animals appear in the fossil record with the flying animal completely formed, and no transitional forms have been found. This is undoubtedly true in cases of the flying reptiles, insects, and bats.

Archaeopteryx is a perfect example of a bird that could not have survived during a half wing, half leg period (see Figures 2.11 and 2.11b). *Archaeopteryx* was a unique bird,

Archaeopteryx: considered to be the oldest known bird — fossils show feathers.

Figure 2.11 What kinds of problems might this hypothetical creature face?

set apart from both reptiles and all other birds, but not a transitional form.

Creationists assert that this lack of transitional forms also applies to man. They say that all the fossil finds are either distinctly man or ape but never part one or part the other. The best information we presently have on fossil man shows him walking upright. When all of this evidence is carefully examined, one may see that all of these creatures were either monkeys, apes, or men.

Are transitional forms necessary to support the creation model? Explain why or why not.

Figure 2.11b Archaeopteryx as it probably looked.

Up Hill or Down Hill

Creation scientists examine the laws of **thermodynamics** in search for information. They note that the first and second laws support their prediction of an original creation. The *first law* states that energy is not being *created or destroyed.* The total amount of energy that is present now never changes and will always be present somewhere in some form, and there is no way that it can be eliminated. This law supports the theory that all life, energy, etc., was created at one time in the past and that creation is finished.

Perhaps the most important law in science is the second law of thermodynamics. The *second law* of thermodynamics is the one law that has been tested more than any other law of science. The second law states that whenever there is an energy change, that is, a chemical action, you can never get all the usable energy you started with back again. When energy is used to do work, some of this energy becomes unavailable to do work again. For example, for every 100 calories in the food you eat, you may be able to do only 50 calories of work. The other 50 calories are lost as heat to the surroundings. All of the original 100 calories of energy are still there somewhere, but half of them have **diffused** into space and cannot be used to do any more work. This law always holds true when physical, chemical or biological systems are operating (see Figures 2.12 and 2.13).

thermodynamics: a science dealing with heat energy.

diffused: scattered into tiny particles.

Figure 2.12 The First Law states that matter and energy can neither be created nor destroyed, but can be changed. The illustration shows matter I in place, with energy holding it together; energy is released from matter I but it is still available somewhere; matter I is now changed to matter II but arranged differently. Matter and energy have been neither created nor destroyed, but they have been changed.

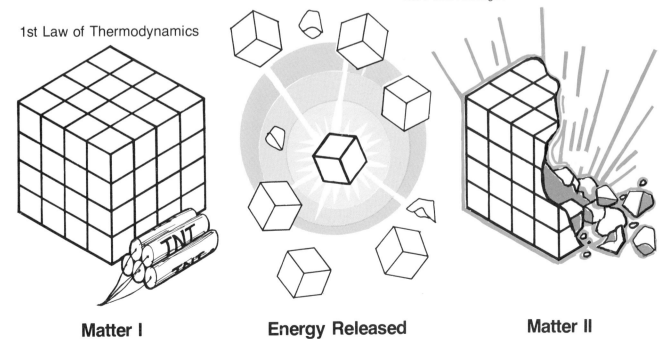

1st Law of Thermodynamics

Matter I   **Energy Released**   **Matter II**

2nd Law of Thermodynamics

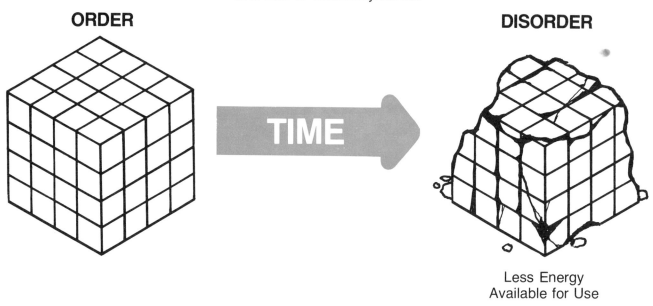

ORDER

TIME

DISORDER

Less Energy
Available for Use

Figure 2.13 The Second Law *says that all energy processes, i.e., chemical, physical, etc., run down when left alone and no new energy is brought in. This running down of a system, or increase in* entropy, *means: a system can be very ordered or complex; but over a period of time it will run down and be less ordered or complex. Some of the energy it had in the first place becomes unavailable; it is still in existence but it can't be used. This is what entropy means, and this is what the Second Law of Thermodynamics is all about. Creation scientists use these facts to show that there is no natural tendency to go from disorder to order or from simple to complex.*

1. Does the *first law* of thermodynamics support the creation model? The evolution model? Explain.

2. Describe the *second law* of thermodynamics the best you can.

3. Does the second law of thermodynamics help the creation model? Explain.

4. Do you think the laws of thermodynamics are strong points for the study of origins? Explain.

Probability

Biochemists have discovered that a single bacterium contains no less than 1,500 **enzymes;** and this does not include other complex chemicals. Enzymes are proteins, each one of which is made up of several hundred amino acids. Each enzyme is very complicated and has a very specific task to do. The drawing below shows a very short portion of an enzyme. A complete enzyme may be 50 to 100 times as large or even larger than this short section containing only five amino acids.

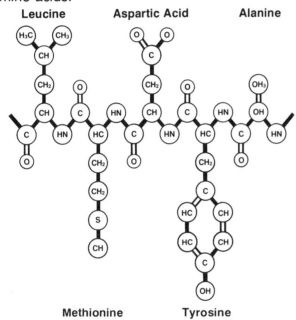

enzymes: organic catalysts that make a bio-chemical reaction go faster.

Figure 2.14 A short portion of an enzyme structure.

The letters in this sentence had to be arranged in a precise sequence in order for this sentence to be written. So it is with enzymes. The 20 different kinds of amino acids which combine in long chains to make enzymes must be arranged in an exact order for each enzyme to have its unique function and to perform efficiently.

When the question of the possibility of these chemicals coming together by **random** processes is examined, many scientists are ready to say that there is no possibility that amino acids would form enzymes by chance.

random: haphazard — chance — aimless — purposeless — without order

Mathematicians look at this from the standpoint of the laws of **probability.** Consider the following: if there are three elements, 1, 2, 3, there will be six possible ways for these to link up: 123, 132, 213, 231, 312, and 321. Imagine that these are enzymes getting together for that very first cell. Each enzyme has a very important and specific job to do. The laws of probability say that there would be one out

probability: a mathematical prediction of the chance of some event occurring.

mathematical factorials: 7! factorial means 1 x 2 x 3 x 4 x 5 x 6 x 7 or 5040.

of six (1:6) chances for that combination to happen accidentally. Using **mathematical factorials**, the probability would look like those below when more units are added.

Figure 2.15 This illustration shows how the laws of probability tend to support the creation view of how life began better than other explanations.

In order for you to get a better idea of just how immense some of these numbers really are, consider the fact that the number of electrons that could be packed into the visible universe (five billion light years in radius) with absolutely no space left vacant amounts to 10^{130}. Imagine how big that number is! And yet the probability of a protein of 200 amino acids (20 different kinds) happening by chance is only one chance out of 10^{260} (20^{200}). Even if by some miracle it did happen, only one single molecule would result, but billions of tons of each of many different protein and DNA molecules would be required for the origin of life.

Origins

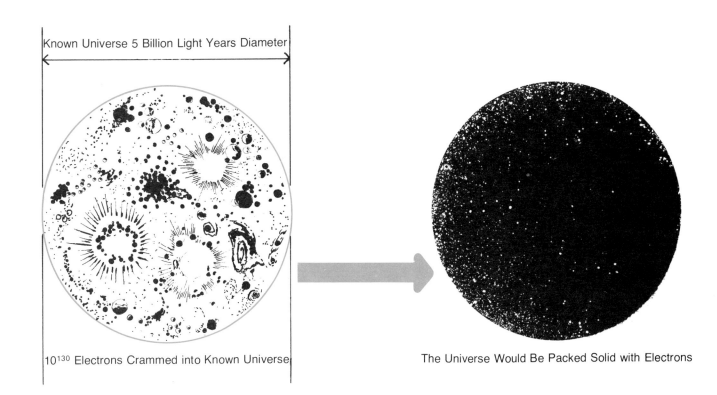

Known Universe 5 Billion Light Years Diameter

10^{130} Electrons Crammed into Known Universe

The Universe Would Be Packed Solid with Electrons

Figure 2.16 *Look at your table of probabilities and consider that only about 10^{130} electrons could be crammed into the known universe.*

If a monkey attempted to type the words, "the theory of creation," and he could type 19 letters every second (there are 19 letters in this phrase), it would require about 10 billion years for him to type it once correctly. Do you know how this was calculated? See if your teacher can help you.

Creationists reason that probability factors alone show that life, as we know it, could never have happened by accident, that is, by the *random* chance processes of nature. They conclude that this could only have come about by an outside power, a creator.

Creation scientists have done experiments recently that seem to show that the process of **natural selection** will not provide a continued change in plant life in a single direction. Consider the diagram on the next page (Figure 2.17).

natural selection: the elimination of the unfit and the survival of the fit in the struggle for existence.

The creationist reasons that if there is in fact reason to doubt that natural selection can produce new *kinds,* then he must assume that creation occurred. Many geneticists think that it is not possible to select from genetic material that isn't there to select from in the first place.

As the scientist views changes in genes and tries to explain why these changes come about, he must consider

Creation

49

mutations. Can mutations be the secret that will allow variations such as we see today? One noted scientist says:

". . . mutations will almost always be harmful; almost always, in fact, they will kill the organism or the cell . . ."[3]

Mutations are not likely to give the variety of life we see today. In fact, if we depended upon the process of *random* mutation for new varieties, considering probability, this would be beyond the thinking of man.

[3]**C.P. Martin,** *American Scientist,* January, 1953, p. 100.

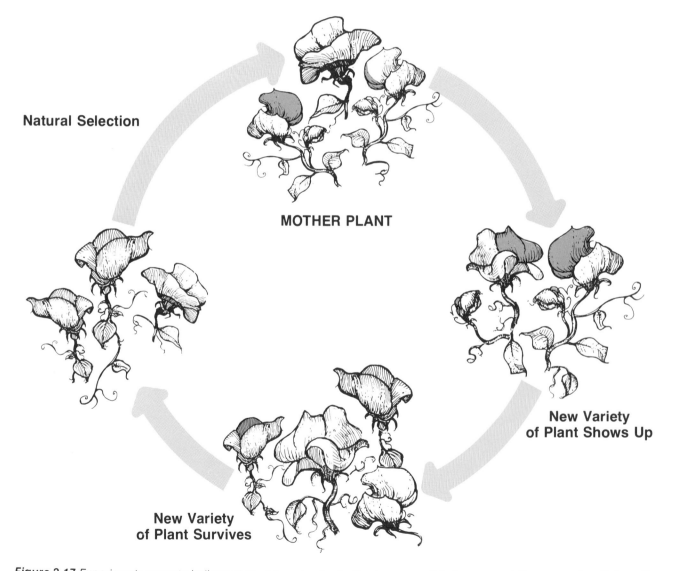

Natural Selection

MOTHER PLANT

**New Variety
of Plant Shows Up**

**New Variety
of Plant Survives**

Figure 2.17 *Experiments seem to indicate that while natural selection is responsible for new varieties appearing, it doesn't continue to go just in one direction. When temperature, moisture and dryness are extreme, natural selection can select back to the original form.*

How Old Is the Earth?

The age of the earth is not the most important thing to the creationist. Whether the earth is very young or very old will not change the creation model. The creationist is free to examine all data on the subject of age. Creation could have occurred in any time period according to the general creation model. Research by creation scientists has come up with startling information in this regard.

One scientist showed that the sedimentary deposits in the oceans are very small (see Figure 2.18), and he has demonstrated that with all factors considered, it would *not* have taken much more than 9,000 years to deposit this sediment.[4] Another scientist[5] calculated the **half life** of the decay of the earth's magnet. He also noted that this mathematical curve showed that the earth could not be over 10,000 years old. Dr. Barnes shows that it would have had a magnetic field similar to a magnetic star.

half life: the length of time for half of the existing quantity of the magnetic field to decay.

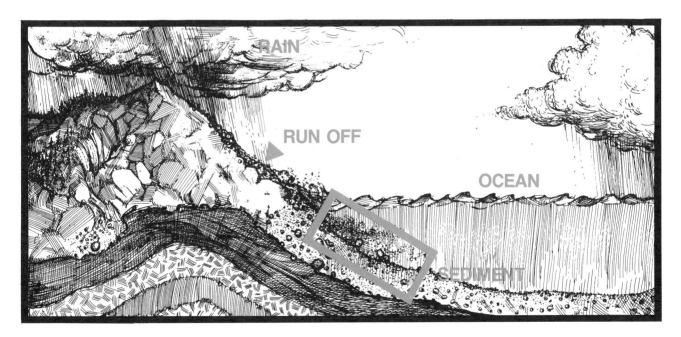

Figure 2.18 Water erodes the continents and deposits the sediments in the ocean. Considering the rapid rate of modern erosion, creationists believe that the thinness of the ocean sediments indicates a young age for the ocean basins.

His research is of the greatest significance — *precise* scientific measurements have been checked repeatedly.

[4]**Stuart Nevins,** "Evolution: The Ocean Says No!", *Impact* No. 8, Institute for Creation Research, San Diego, California, 1973.

[5]**Thomas G. Barnes,** *Origin and Destiny of the Earth's Magnetic Field,* Creation-Life Publishers, San Diego, California, 1973.

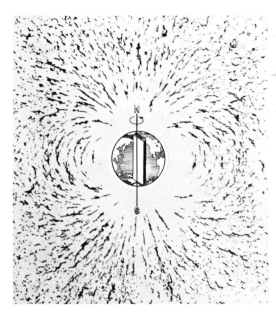

Figure 2.19 The earth acts as a huge magnet.

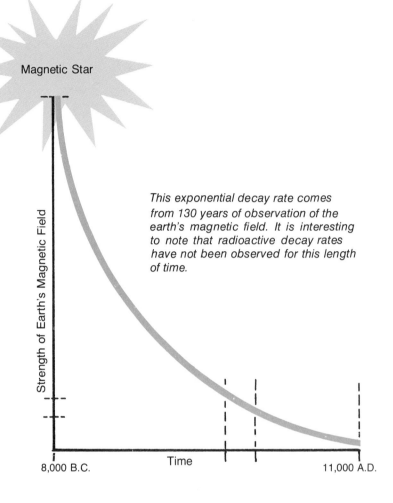

Magnetic Star

Strength of Earth's Magnetic Field

This exponential decay rate comes from 130 years of observation of the earth's magnetic field. It is interesting to note that radioactive decay rates have not been observed for this length of time.

Time

8,000 B.C.   11,000 A.D.

Figure 2.20 This diagram shows the magnetic decay curve predicted by Dr. Thomas Barnes, University of Texas, El Paso.

Figure 2.21
Radioactive time clocks work just like most clocks work. We need to know how much radioactivity and products there were in the beginning and how much there are now.

for accuracy, and each time they have been proved correct.

Another interesting study by a scientist from the University of Utah indicated that the earth might be young.[6] Remember the uranium clock from the Evolution Model (Fig. 2.21)? This study showed that the two kinds of uranium clocks, U^{238}-Pb^{206} and U^{235}-Pb^{207}, may not have been running as long as some scientists thought. In fact, the data show that these clocks give evidence of a very young earth, not a very old earth. We will get more deeply into this

[6]**M.A. Cook,** *Prehistory and Earth Models,* Max Parrish and Co., Ltd., London, 1966.

Origins

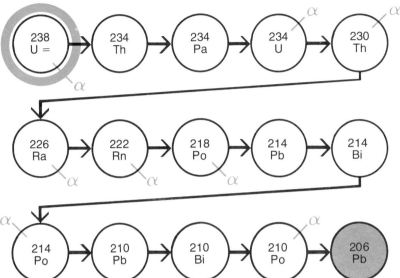

Figure 2.22 *This diagram shows how uranium (U-238) decays to lead (Pb-206). Creation scientists show this clock can give young ages more logically than old ages. They also show that these clocks may not always decay at a constant rate. A deeper discussion of this matter is found in the module on "Time And Earth History."*

A Model for Design

Creation scientists look at all living substances and reason that they show creative design. All life was designed to function a certain way and for a specific purpose. We will consider a living cell and one of its tiny parts as a first step in considering creative design (see Figure 2.23).

Scientists know that such a cell is very complex. It has the power to reproduce itself; it carries hereditary traits; it manufactures its own DNA; it has control mechanisms for its very powerful enzymes. Biologists know that some enzymes could even destroy the cell if they went out of control. The cell has an important limiting membrane, one that allows only the right things into the cell and rejects the others; this membrane also allows only the right things out of the cell and retains the others. The cell has a controlling nucleus that tells it precisely what to do; it has a power converter in the mighty **mitochondria**, that manufactures energy for the cell's chemical factory. This very tiny power plant is so complex that the nature of it is boggling to the minds of scientists (see Figure 2.24).

The creation scientist asks the question, "Could this complex cell system have ever happened through a long series of chance accidental processes? Does the system

mitochondria (singular, mitochondrion):
Chemical power converters essential for the release of energy to the cell.

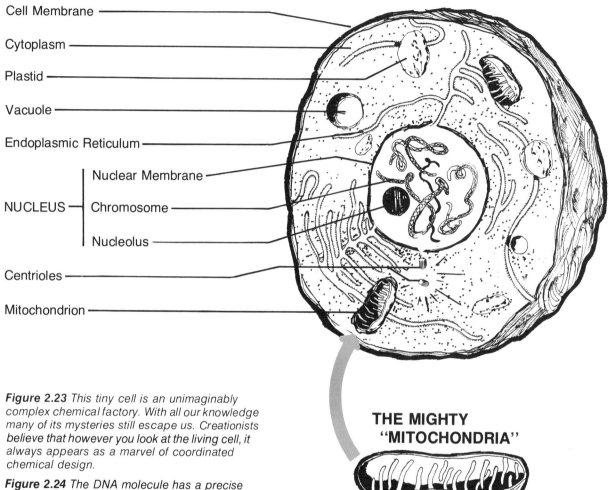

Cell Membrane

Cytoplasm

Plastid

Vacuole

Endoplasmic Reticulum

NUCLEUS — Nuclear Membrane

Chromosome

Nucleolus

Centrioles

Mitochondrion

THE MIGHTY "MITOCHONDRIA"

Figure 2.23 *This tiny cell is an unimaginably complex chemical factory. With all our knowledge many of its mysteries still escape us. Creationists believe that however you look at the living cell, it always appears as a marvel of coordinated chemical design.*

Figure 2.24 *The DNA molecule has a precise coding arrangement. Each part of the code is in precise order for a specific protein molecule.*

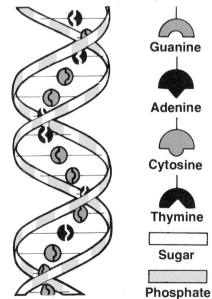

Guanine

Adenine

Cytosine

Thymine

Sugar

Phosphate

have a purpose? Does it show intricate design?'' In this respect, it seems that the probability of this happening by accident is ''0''.

It's Up to You

You have now heard both models in their *general terms.* There is much more on both sides to consider. You have to be the judge. Which will you accept? As you read more and thus add more information to your bank of knowledge, you will be in a better position for decision making. Your teacher can help you to understand some of this very complex science better. He will also be able to point you to good books

[7]**P.T. Mora,** "The Folly of Probability," in *The Origins of Prebiological Systems and of Their Molecular Matrices,* **S.W. Fox,** Ed., Academic Press, New York, 1965.

relating to origins. We might caution also that the writings of some scientists are biased; you will have to sort out what is fact and what is assumption and then judge for yourself.

1. With the information you now have, name two parts of the evolution model that seem most doubtful to you.

2. With the information you now have, name two parts of the creation model that seem most doubtful to you.

3. What three *major* assumptions must the evolutionist make if his model is going to stand?

4. What three *major* assumptions must the creationist make if his model is going to stand?

5. In the evolution of reptiles to birds, what assumptions must be made about wings in this model?

6. How would the creation model explain this same problem (#5)?

7. How are the *coacervate* and *proteinoid* hypotheses related to evolutionary theory?

8. How would biological isolation help new varieties or species to occur?

9. Does biological isolation contradict the creation model? Yes? No? Explain.

10. What geologic evidence seems to support each model (Evolution, Creation)?

11. Show how index fossils are used to date strata.

BIBLIOGRAPHY

Evolution Books

1. **Gastonguay, Paul R.,** *Evolution for Everyone,* Bobbs Merrill Co., Inc., 1974 (Biological Science Curriculum Study), 213 pp.

*2. **Marquand, Josephine,** *Life: Its Nature, Origins and Distribution,* W. W. Norton & Company, Inc., New York, 1971, 96 pp.

*3. **Hodge, Paul W.,** *Concepts of the Universe,* McGraw-Hill Book Company, New York, 1969, 125 pp.

*4. **Darwin, Charles,** *Introduction to Origin of Species,* Everyman's Library, E. P. Dutton and Co., Inc., New York.

*5. **Blum, Harold F.,** *Time's Arrow and Evolution,* Princeton University Press, Princeton, New Jersey, 1968, 232 pp.

6. **Oram, Raymond F.,** *Biology: Living Systems,* Charles E. Merrill Pub. Co., Columbus, Ohio, 1973, 784 pp.

*7. **Day, M. H.,** *The Fossil History of Man,* Oxford University Press, Ely House, London W.I., 16 pp.

Creation Books

1. **Morris, Henry M.,** *Scientific Creationism,* Creation-Life Publishers, San Diego, 1974, 217 pp.

2. **Gish, Duane T.,** *Evolution: The Fossils Say No!,* Creation-Life Publishers, San Diego, 1973, 129 pp.

*3. **Barnes, Thomas G.,** *Origin and Destiny of the Earth's Magnetic Field,* Institute for Creation Research, San Diego, 1973, 64 pp.

*4. **Gish, Duane T.,** *Speculations and Experiments on the Origin of Life,* Institute for Creation Research, 1972, 41 pp.

*5. **Lammerts, W. E.,** Ed., *Scientific Studies in Special Creation,* Presbyterian and Reformed Co., Philadelphia, Pa., 1971, 343 pp.

*6. **Slusher, Harold S.,** *Critique of Radiometric Dating,* Institute for Creation Research, San Diego, 1973, 46 pp.

7. **Moore, John N.** and **Slusher, Harold S.,** Eds., *Biology: A Search for Order in Complexity,* Zondervan, Grand Rapids, Mi, 1970, 548 pp.

8. **Morris, Henry M.** and **Gish, Duane T.,** *The Battle for Creation,* Creation-Life Publishers, San Diego, 1976, 321 pp.

*9. **Clark, Marlyn E.,** *Our Amazing Circulatory System,* Creation-Life Publishers San Diego, 1976, 66 pp.

*Books that are somewhat technical in nature.

CREDITS

Designed and produced by Tim Ravenna and Brad Barrett.

Chapter One

Figure 1.1, The Bettman Archive. **Figure 1.2,** Jay Wegter, Tim Ravenna. **Figure 1.2,** Jay Wegter, Tim Ravenna. **Figure 1.3,** Tim Ravenna. **Figure 1.4,** from the experiments of Dr. H. B. D. Kettlewell, University of Oxford. **Figure 1.5,** squirrels, Jay Wegter; maps, Tim Ravenna. **Figure 1.6,** Jay Wegter. **Figure 1.7,** Jay Wegter. **Figure 1.8,** Tim Ravenna. **Figure 1.9a,** Ted Hansen. **Figure 1.9b,** University of California at San Diego. **Figure 1.10,** Tim Ravenna. **Figure 1.11,** Chris Roth. **Figure 1.12,** Tim Ravenna. **Figure 1.13,** Ted Hansen, Tim Ravenna, Jay Wegter. **Figure 1.14,** Jay Wegter. **Figure 1.15,** Tim Ravenna. **Figure 1.16,** Jay Wegter. **Figure 1.17,** Tim Ravenna. **Figure 1.18,** Tim Ravenna, Jay Wegter. **Figure 1.19,** Tim Ravenna, **Figure 1.20,** Tim Ravenna. **Figure 1.21,** Jay Wegter. **Figure 1.22,** Tim Ravenna. **Figure 1.23,** Jay Wegter. **Figure 1.24,** Jay Wegter. **Figure 1.25,** Jay Wegter.

Chapter Two

Figure 2.1, Jay Wegter. **Figure 2.2,** Tim Ravenna. **Figure 2.3,** Tim Ravenna, Jay Wegter. **Figure 2.4,** Jay Wegter. **Figure 2.5,** Tim Ravenna. **Figure 2.6,** courtesy of the American Museum of Natural History. **Figure 2.7,** Marvin Ross. **Figure 2.8,** Tim Ravenna. **Figure 2.9,** Jay Wegter. **Figure 2.10,** Jay Wegter. **Figure 2.11** Tim Ravenna. **Figure 2.11b,** from Organic Evolution, R. S. Lull, The Macmillan Co. **Figure 2.12,** Tim Ravenna. **Figure 2.13,** Tim Ravenna. **Figure 2.14,** Ted Hansen. **Figure 2.15,** John Chong. **Figure 2.16,** Tim Ravenna, Chris Roth. **Figure 2.17,** Jay Wegter. **Figure 2.18,** Jay Wegter. **Figure 2.19,** Joe Austin. **Figure 2.20,** Tim Ravenna, Joe Austin. **Figure 2.21,** Tim Ravenna. **Figure 2.22,** Tim Ravenna. **Figure 2.23,** Chris Roth. **Figure 2.24,** Tim Ravenna. Photograph on page v, Hale Observatories.